My Big Book of
Trucks,
Planes
and Trains

MY BIG BOOK OF TRUCKS, PLANES AND TRAINS

A HUTCHINSON BOOK ISBN 978 0 857 54000 3

First published in Great Britain by Hutchinson,
an imprint of Random House Children's Books
A Random House Group Company

Well Done, Dougal! first published by Red Fox Picture Books, 2010
Dougal the Digger first published by Red Fox Picture Books, 2009
Night Flight for the Little Red Train first published by Red Fox Picture Books, 2005
'All Kinds of Cars' first published in 2002 by Hutchinson in *Ben's Big Book of Cars*
Big Truck first published by Hutchinson, 2000
Aeroplane first published by Hutchinson, 2000
Blue Tractor first published by Julia MacRae Books, 1999
This edition published as a collection 2010

1 3 5 7 9 10 8 6 4 2

Hutchinson books are published by Random House Children's Books,
61-63 Uxbridge Road, London W5 5SA

Book designed by Clair Lansley
Cover designed by Alison Gadsby

www.**rbooks**.co.uk
www.**kids**at**random**.co.uk
Addresses for companies within The Random House Group Limited
can be found at: www.randomhouse.co.uk/offices.htm

THE RANDOM HOUSE GROUP Limited Reg. No. 954009
A CIP catalogue record for this book is available from the British Library.
Printed in China

My Big Book of Trucks, Planes and Trains

Benedict Blathwayt

Hutchinson

Contents

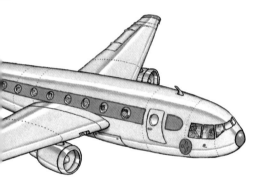

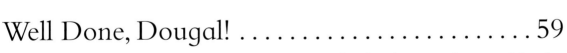

Dougal the Digger

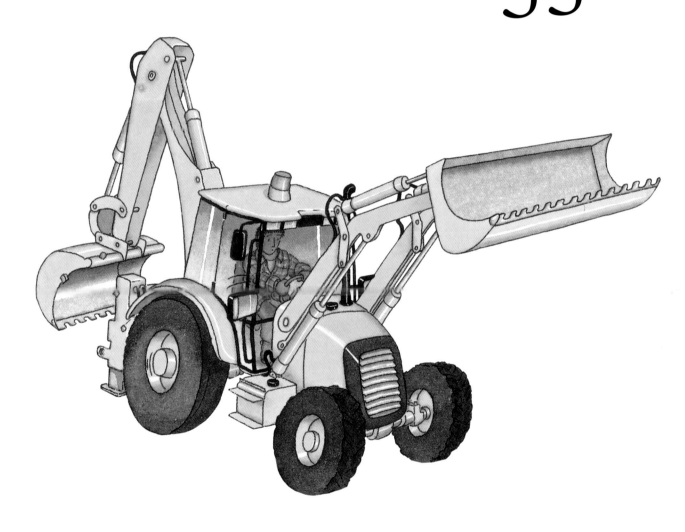

Dougal the Digger arrived at the building site.

"There are lots of old buildings to be knocked down," said the foreman to Dougal's driver.

Dougal set to work at once. What a lot of noise and dust! The foreman shut his dog Patch in a shed so he would be safe.

"You be good and stay in there," he said.

Dougal scooped up lots of rubble and tipped it into big trucks.

"STOP!" shouted the foreman, waving a red flag. "Wait there! We are knocking down a very tall building."

CRASH!

The walls came tumbling down in a cloud of dust.

Now there was a huge new pile of rubble for Dougal to clear away.
"Has anyone seen my dog Patch?" asked the foreman.
Nobody had seen Patch.

Everyone helped look for Patch. But Patch was gone!

Then the foreman thought he heard the sound of a dog barking coming from inside a big pile of rubble.

"That sounds just like Patch!" he said.

Very carefully, Dougal dug away the rubble. The barking grew LOUDER AND **LOUDER.**

There was Patch, safe and sound!

   He had been hiding inside a piece of concrete pipe. How
pleased he was to see everyone. **Well done, Dougal!**

Aeroplane

Dan and his mother hurry out to the aeroplane.

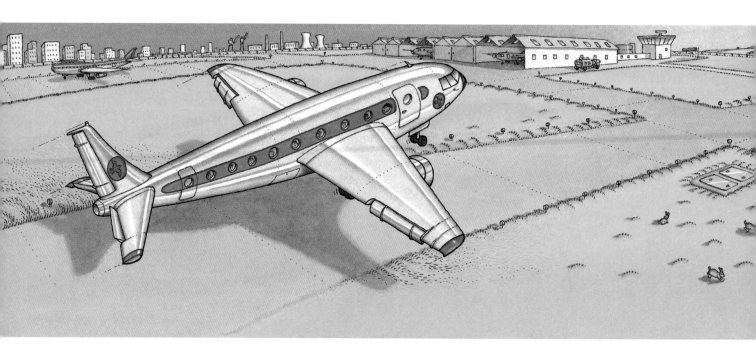

They roar down the runway and take off.

14

Then they climb up, up, up into the sky.

How excited Dan feels flying above the clouds!

Night Flight for the Little Red Train

Duffy the engine driver hurried off to get the Little Red Train ready for an important journey.

"Take care of your new uniform," his wife called after him.

Duffy and the Little Red Train were travelling overnight to Scotland; passengers and post had to be there by sunrise.

Jack the guard was at the engine shed to help Duffy with the carriages. They hooked Jack's van to the very back of the train.

Duffy was in a terrible rush. "Every minute counts," he said. "We must be in Scotland by sunrise."

At the station a crowd of passengers waited on the platform.

Duffy and Jack were very busy: there were lots of letters and parcels to be loaded onto the train.

Duffy smiled. "Somebody's birthday somewhere!" he said, picking up a card.

"It will be dark soon," said Jack. "Don't forget to fix the headlamp so we can see where we are going."

At last they were ready to leave.

Duffy blew the whistle and the Little Red Train steamed out of the station.

Whoo…oo…eee!

*Fuff…chuff…
fuff…chuff…fuff
…chuff…chuff!*

Click clack, clicketty clack,

clicketty clicketty clack!

Soon the bright lights of the city were far behind them.

But the moon was out and there was still lots to see.

Then the Little Red Train entered a long, dark tunnel.

Duffy suddenly realized he had forgotten something very important: "The headlamp!" he cried. "It's still in Jack's van!"

Without light Duffy couldn't see where they were going. But stopping to fit the lamp would take too much time, and they would never reach Scotland by sunrise.

There was only one thing to do . . .

Duffy climbed onto the roof and back along the carriages to Jack's van.

He had to hold on tight.

Then Duffy crawled carefully back again to fix the headlamp at the very front.

The Little Red Train flew along the tracks at a tremendous speed.

Ticketty tack ticketty tack ticketty tack . . .

Now I can see what lies ahead, thought Duffy, and whatever is ahead can see us coming . . .

The next morning the Little Red Train pulled into the station just as the sun was rising.

Click clack . . . clacketty clack . . . clacketty clacketty . . . CLUNK!

"We made it! And right on time," said Duffy.

"But look at you!" said Jack. "Whatever happened?"

"Bit of a problem with the headlamp," Duffy said, "but I soon took care of it."

"Which is more than you can say about your uniform!" grinned Jack.

Whoo-oo-oosh! hissed the smoke and smuts from the Little Red Train's funnel.

Whoo-oo-oossssssssssh!

Blue Tractor

Ted drives his blue tractor into the farmyard . . .

and hooks a trailer on the back.

In the field he loads up the bales of straw.

Now back to the farm for tea!

All Kinds of CARS

All Kinds of Cars

Three-wheeler
Two wheels at the back and one at the front

Saloon
A smart car to drive to work

People carrier
Enough seats for a big family

Estate
Lots of room in the back

Van
For small deliveries and light loads

Hatchback
A smaller version
of the estate car

Four-wheel drive
The engine controls all four wheels
so it is easy to drive over bumpy
ground

Convertible
The roof can go
up or down

Pick-up truck
Strong enough for tough use

Sports car
Goes very fast!

33

On the Road

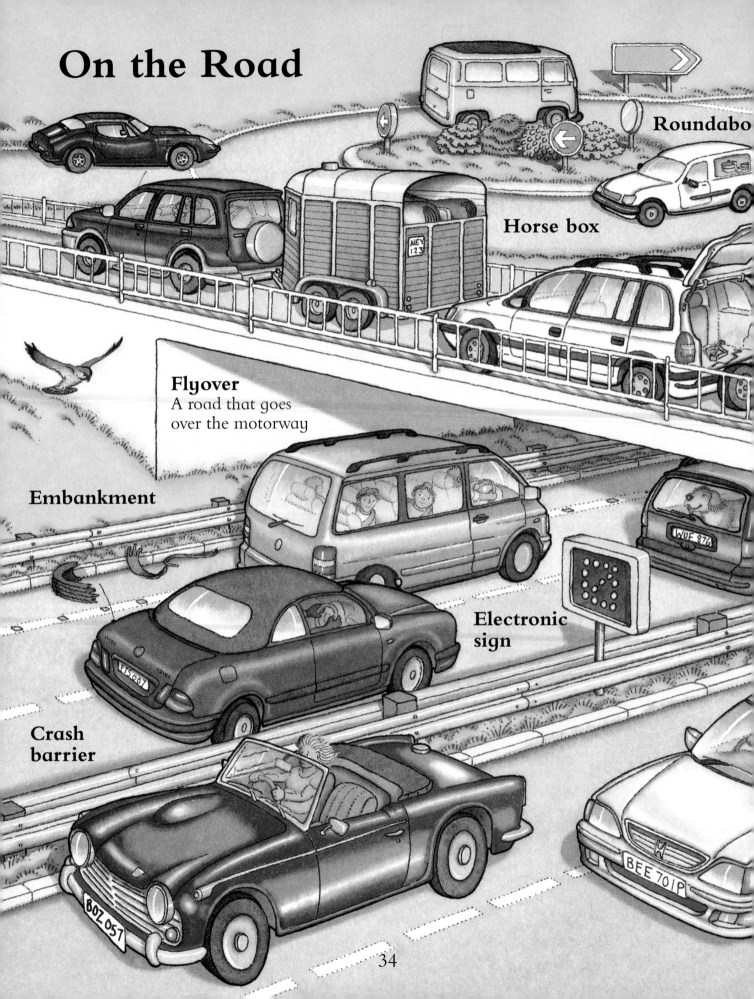

Roundabo

Horse box

Flyover
A road that goes
over the motorway

Embankment

Electronic
sign

Crash
barrier

Cattle bridge

Caravan

Police car

Emergency telephone

Hard shoulder

Taking a Break

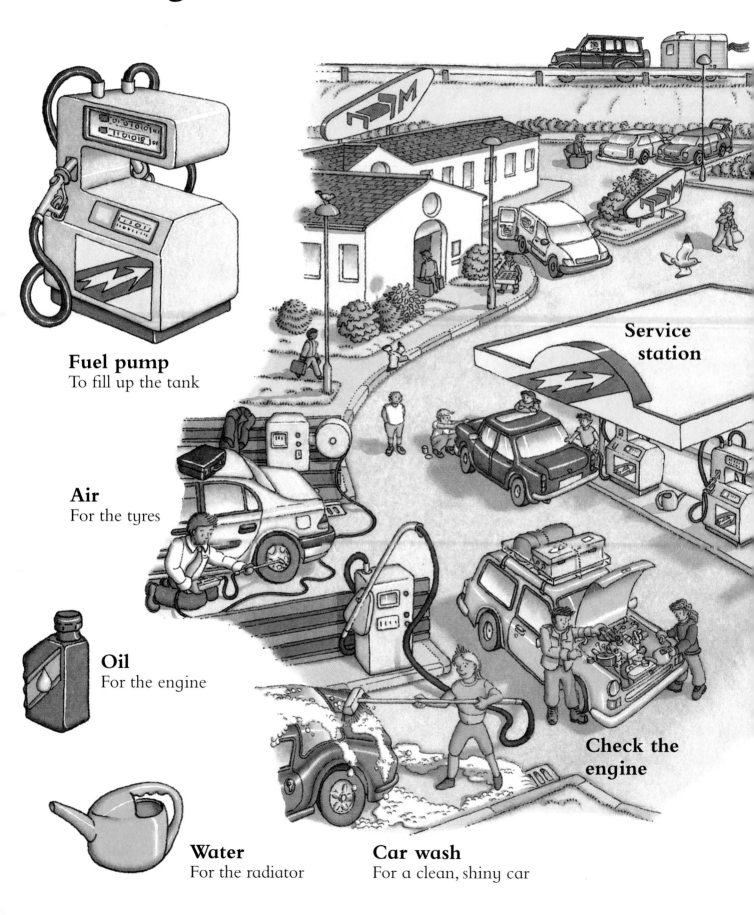

Fuel pump
To fill up the tank

Air
For the tyres

Oil
For the engine

Water
For the radiator

Car wash
For a clean, shiny car

Service station

Check the engine

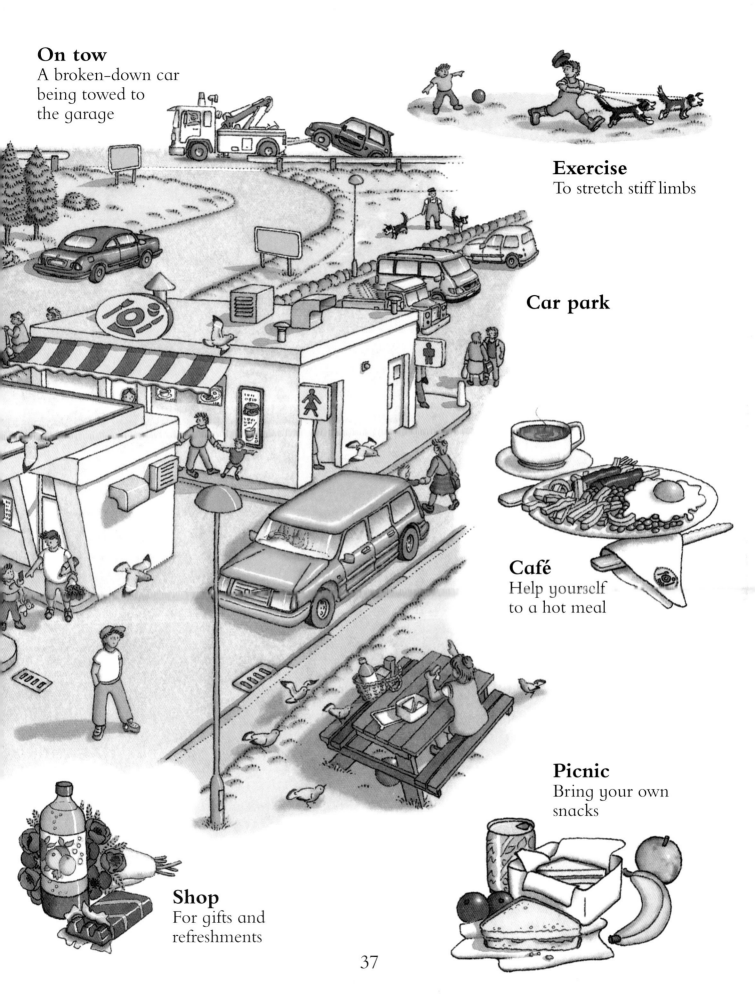

On tow
A broken-down car being towed to the garage

Exercise
To stretch stiff limbs

Car park

Café
Help yourself to a hot meal

Picnic
Bring your own snacks

Shop
For gifts and refreshments

37

At the Garage

Scrap metal
Can be melted down and used again

Workshop
Where cars are repaired

Waste oil
Can be used again

Breakdown truck
To tow broken-down cars

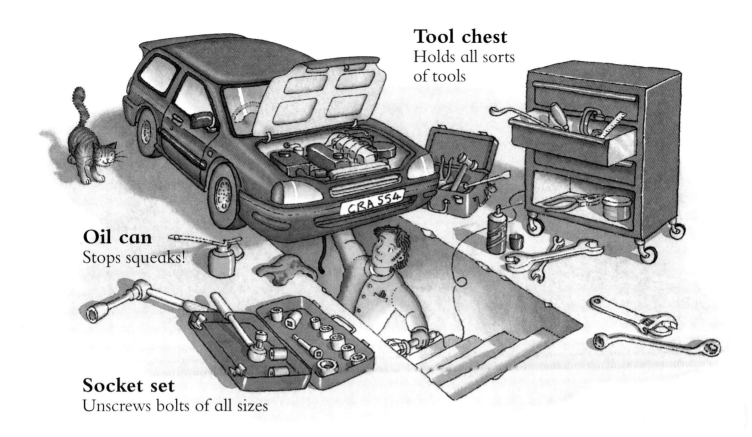

Tool chest
Holds all sorts
of tools

Oil can
Stops squeaks!

Socket set
Unscrews bolts of all sizes

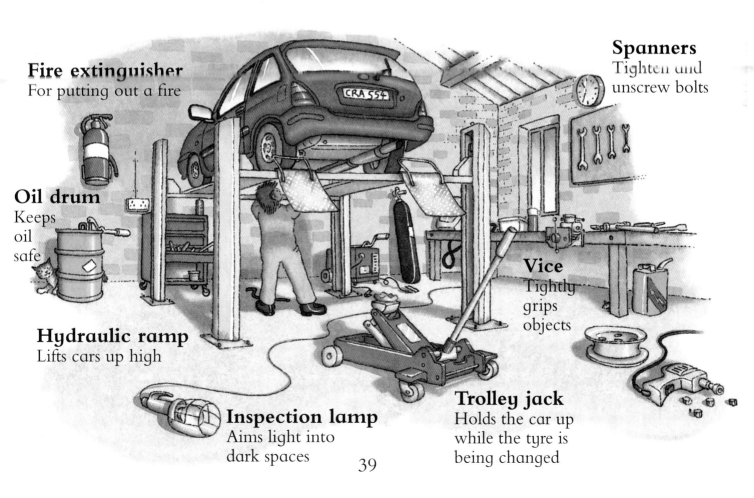

Fire extinguisher
For putting out a fire

Oil drum
Keeps
oil
safe

Hydraulic ramp
Lifts cars up high

Inspection lamp
Aims light into
dark spaces

Spanners
Tighten and
unscrew bolts

Vice
Tightly
grips
objects

Trolley jack
Holds the car up
while the tyre is
being changed

Parts of the Car

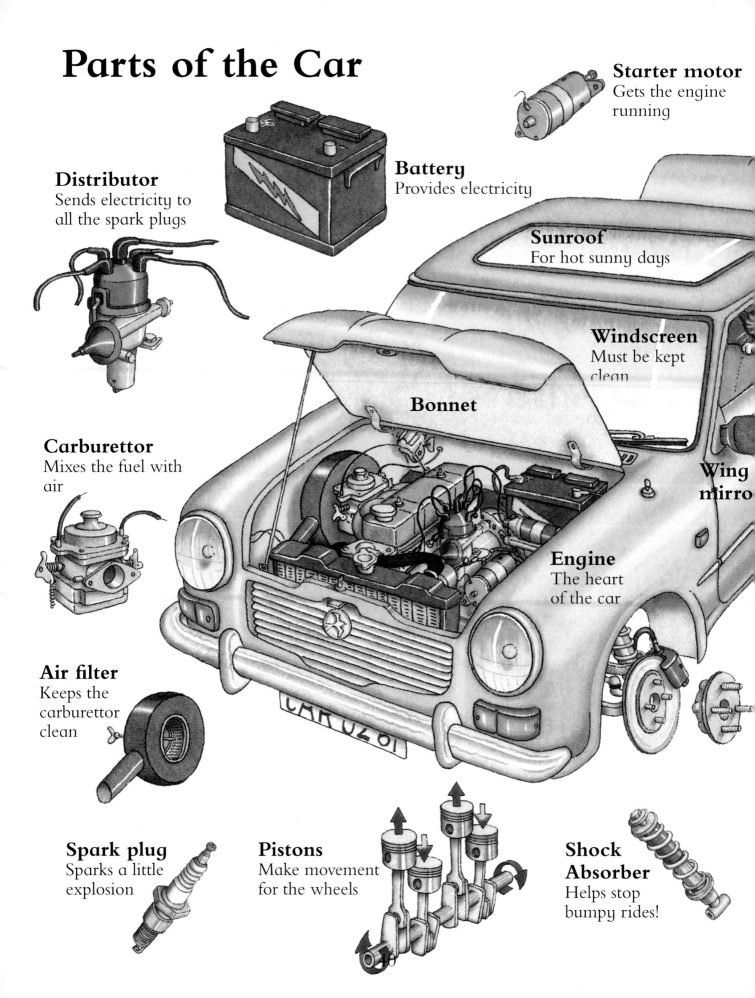

Starter motor
Gets the engine running

Distributor
Sends electricity to all the spark plugs

Battery
Provides electricity

Sunroof
For hot sunny days

Windscreen
Must be kept clean

Bonnet

Wing mirror

Carburettor
Mixes the fuel with air

Engine
The heart of the car

Air filter
Keeps the carburettor clean

Spark plug
Sparks a little explosion

Pistons
Make movement for the wheels

Shock Absorber
Helps stop bumpy rides!

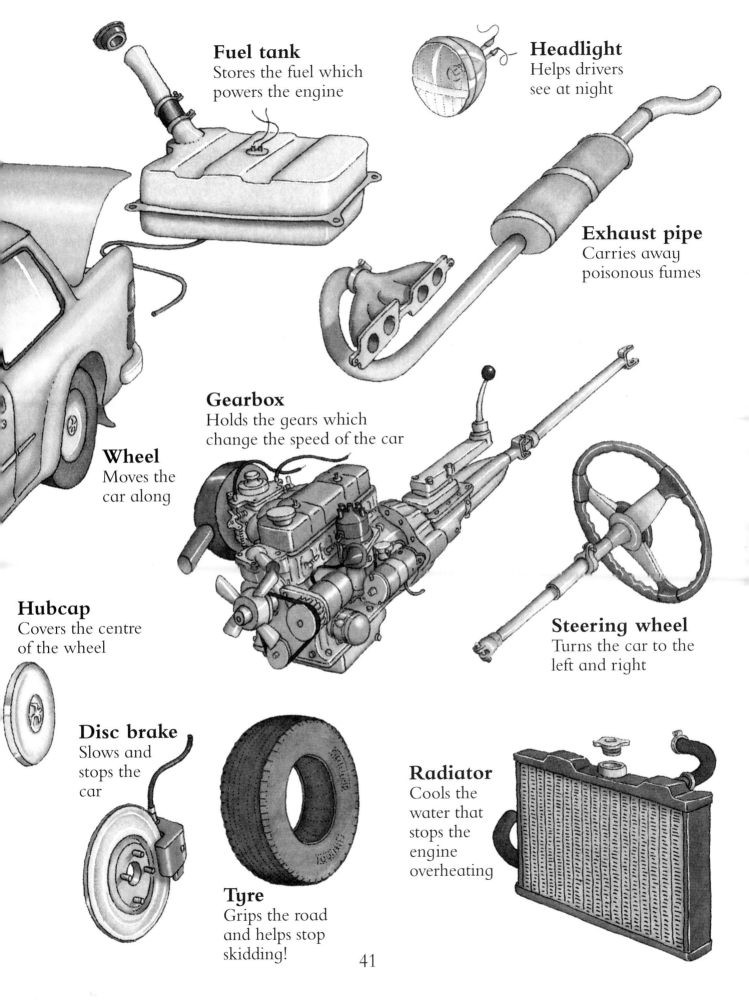

Fuel tank
Stores the fuel which powers the engine

Headlight
Helps drivers see at night

Exhaust pipe
Carries away poisonous fumes

Gearbox
Holds the gears which change the speed of the car

Wheel
Moves the car along

Steering wheel
Turns the car to the left and right

Hubcap
Covers the centre of the wheel

Disc brake
Slows and stops the car

Tyre
Grips the road and helps stop skidding!

Radiator
Cools the water that stops the engine overheating

41

First Cars

The Panhard-Levassor was one of the first cars to have an engine at the front, a gearbox, four wheels rather than three and a proper steering wheel.

Model T Ford "Tin Lizzie", 1908

Bugatti Type 35, 1924

Early cars were very expensive, difficult to drive and unreliable. In 1908 Henry Ford designed a car that everyone could afford. His factories produced over 23 million Model T Fords.

Some drivers wanted only speed and excitement from their cars, others were happy with comfort and reliability.

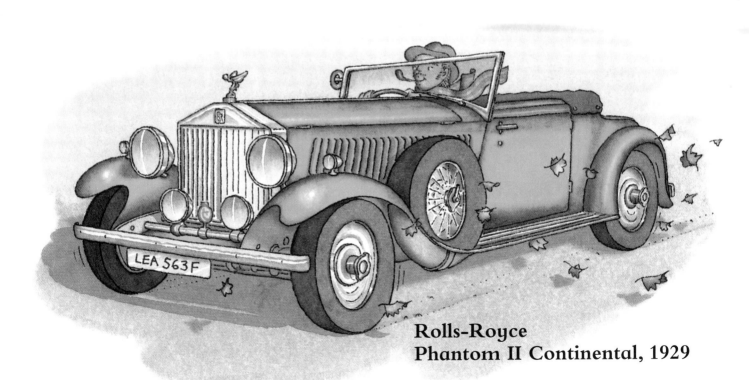

Rolls-Royce
Phantom II Continental, 1929

43

Cars that Race

Dragster
Very noisy and very fast

Go-cart
Small, low to the
ground and lots
of fun!

Stock car
Specially adapted for rough racing,
these cars often crash!

Sports car
Sports car races
can last a whole
day and night

Touring car
Ordinary cars with specially tuned
engines to make them go fast

Rally car
Must be strong enough
for the roughest of tracks

Grand Prix racer
A magnificent racing
machine with a big engine,
big tyres and a long,
smooth body

Rally Car Racing

Splashing through the water

Bouncing over bumpy ground

Rally cars race one by one over a course that is often narrow and rough. The fastest time wins!

START

Skidding on snow

Speeding round corners

47

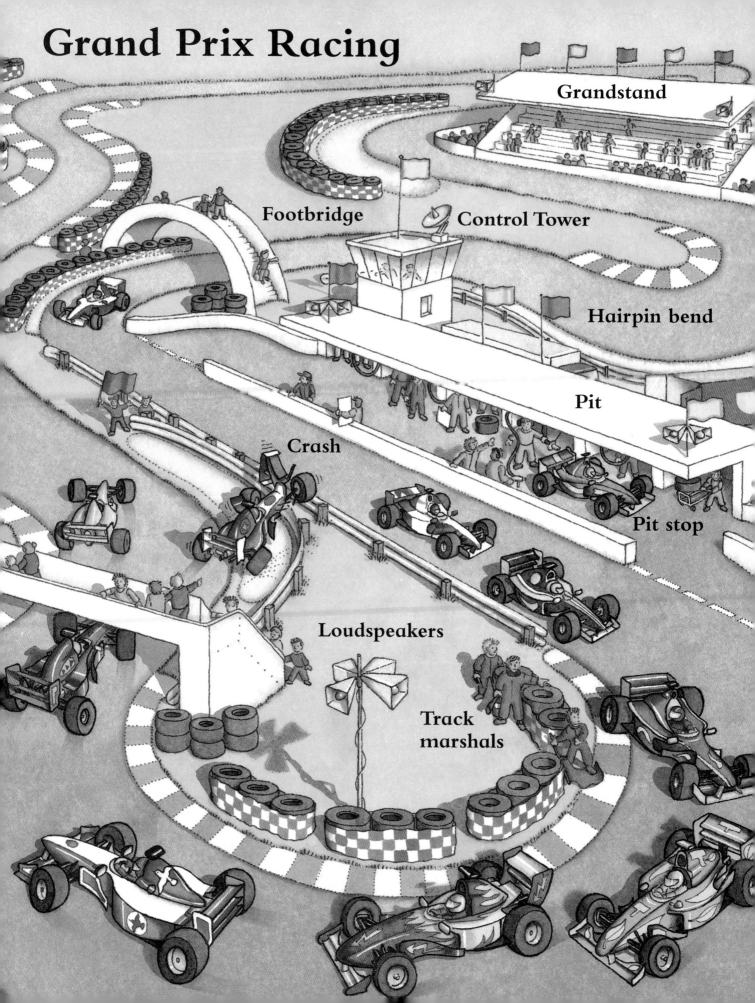

Grand Prix Racing

Grandstand

Footbridge

Control Tower

Hairpin bend

Pit

Crash

Pit stop

Loudspeakers

Track
marshals

Getting ready to race

Out on the circuit

**Into the pit for more fuel
and a quick tyre change**

49

Classic Cars

Popular in their day and
still seen on the road today!

Morris Mini Minor
Very small and
easy to park

Volkswagen Van
The whole family can
go on holiday

Volkswagen Beetle
Designed by Ferdinand Porsche

Austin Healey "Frogeye" Sprite
A classic British sports car

Citroën DS "Décapotable" (convertible)
Stylish, with a special suspension

Morris Minor
Very reliable

Morris Minor Traveller
Reliable with lots of room

SAAB 46
Designed for the cold
Swedish winters

Ford Escort RS
Won lots of rallies
in its time

Citroën 2CV "Deux Chevaux"
(two horsepower)
Ideal for getting the wind in your hair!

Fiat 500 "Topolino"
(little mouse)
A perfect little city car

Unusual Cars

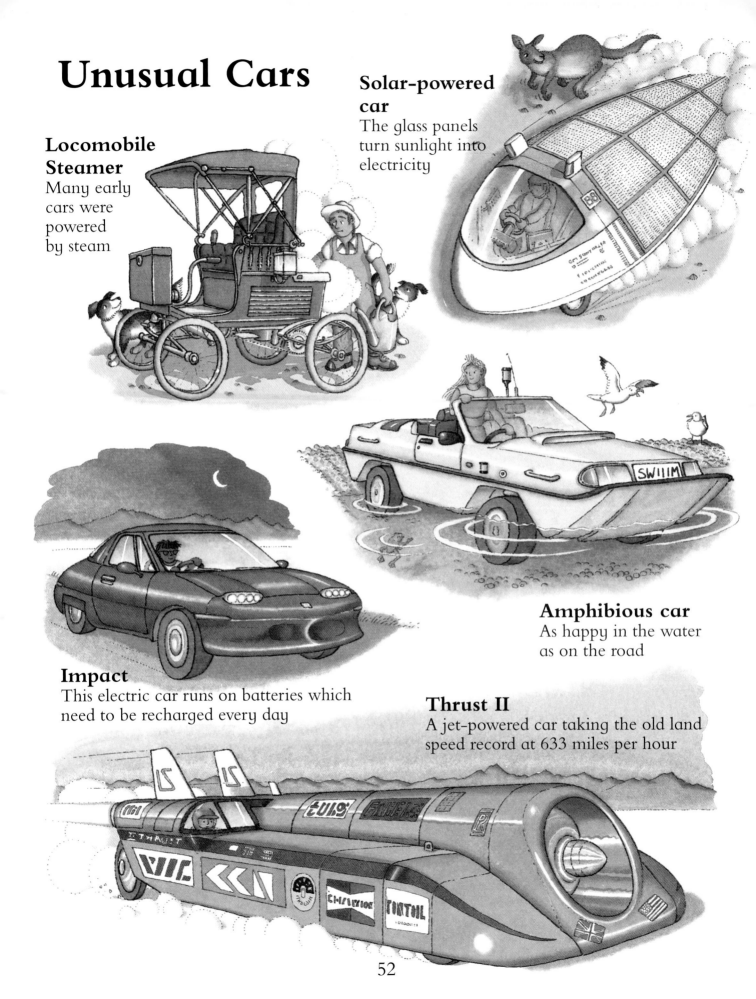

Solar-powered car
The glass panels turn sunlight into electricity

Locomobile Steamer
Many early cars were powered by steam

Amphibious car
As happy in the water as on the road

Impact
This electric car runs on batteries which need to be recharged every day

Thrust II
A jet-powered car taking the old land speed record at 633 miles per hour

"Stretched" Limousine
Often carries famous people!

Trojan Bubble Car
A tiny three-wheeled novelty car

Lunar Rover
"Moon Buggy"
The first car on the moon!

Big Truck

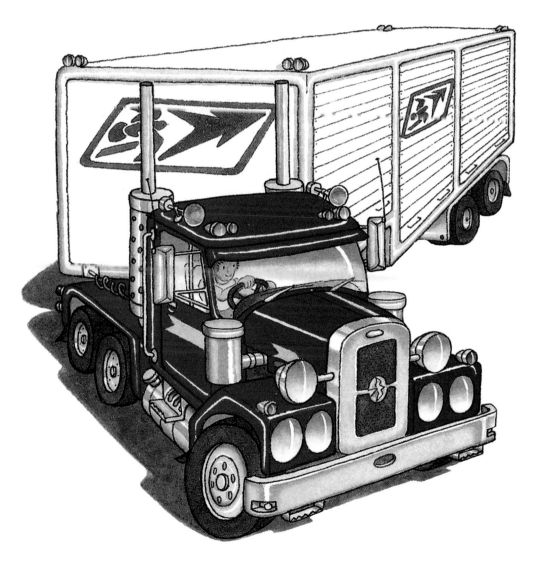

Joe and his truck have a long way to go.

Joe loves his job, the miles pass quickly.

Go slowly, Joe, on the dangerous mountain road!

Joe is glad when they arrive at the docks.

Well Done, Dougal!

Dougal the Digger was down at the harbour digging a trench for new drains.

The foreman and his dog Patch were there too.

Some children from the village were going fishing. Patch wanted to go as well.

"Keep clear of the red warning flags," the harbour master reminded them. "It gets very shallow out there at low tide."

In the morning the tide came right in.

In the afternoon the tide began to go out again.

Suddenly there was a lot of shouting and barking from the middle of the bay. On their way home, the children had run aground.

"That mud is deep and dangerous stuff," said the harbour master, shaking his head. "Unless we get them off soon they'll be stuck until tonight's high tide – and it's going to get very dark and cold out there."

They **threw** a long rope to the boat.

They all tried to pull the boat off the mud – but it was hopeless.

They
pulled and pulled and pulled
. . . but the boat stayed stuck.

Then the harbour master had an idea. He tied the rope to the back of Dougal.

"It's up to you now, Dougal," he said.

Dougal's fat tyres gripped the harbour road. The rope grew tighter and tighter and tighter.

Dougal's engine ROARED . . .

Then SHLOOOP!

The boat suddenly slid off the mud into the water with a great big SPLASH!

"Hooray!" shouted everyone when the children were safely back on dry land.

"All thanks to Dougal!" smiled the harbour master.

"Yes," said the children. "**Well done, Dougal!**"

Woof, woof! barked Patch.

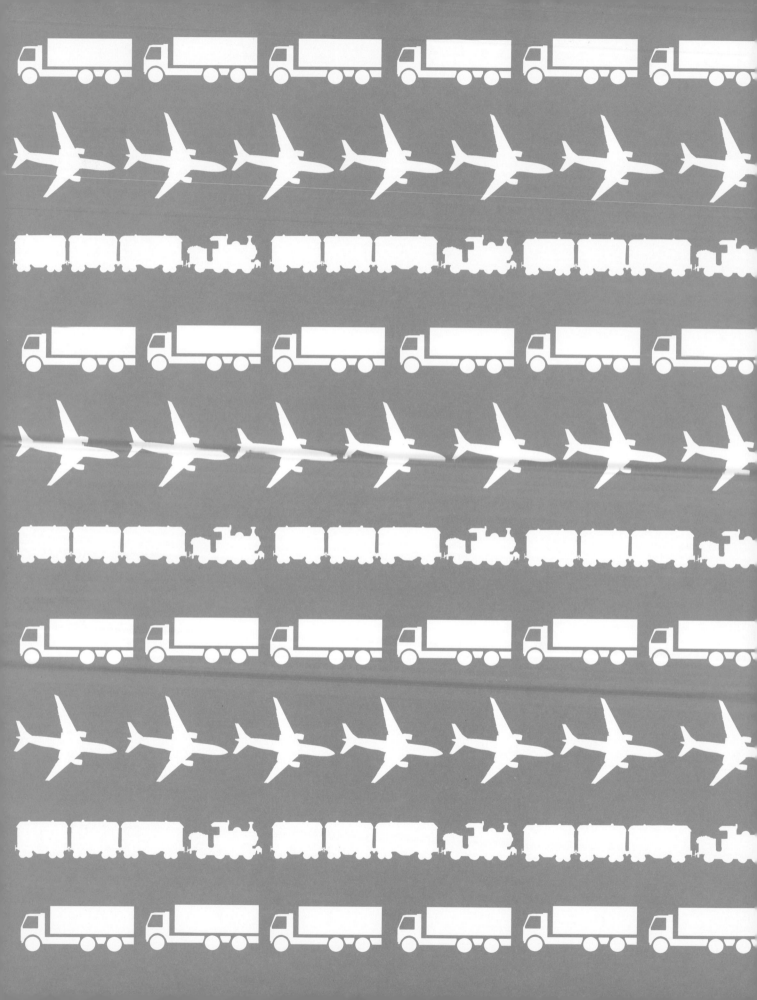